Back to Basics

SCIENCE

for 9–10 year olds

Godfrey Hall

The skeleton

Bone is very hard, but when babies are born their bones are soft and rubbery. As children get older their bones turn harder. In very old people the bones may become brittle and can be easily broken. Look at this skeleton and use the words below to name the bones.

skull   rib   femur   patella   humerus   scapula

fibula   clavicle   tibia   radius   ulna   pelvis   spine

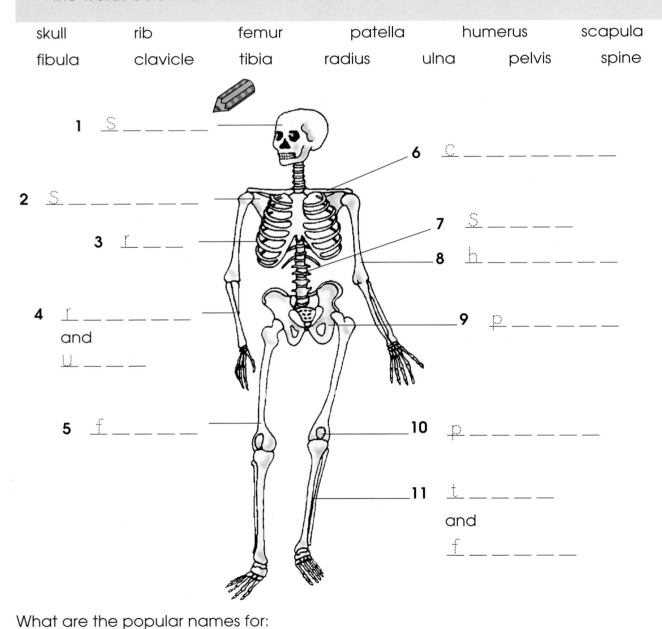

1   S _ _ _ _ _

2   S _ _ _ _ _ _

3   r _ _ _

4   r _ _ _ _ _ _
    and
    u _ _ _

5   f _ _ _ _

6   c _ _ _ _ _ _ _

7   S _ _ _ _

8   h _ _ _ _ _ _

9   p _ _ _ _ _

10 p _ _ _ _ _ _

11 t _ _ _ _
    and
    f _ _ _ _ _

What are the popular names for:

1   The scapula ....

2   The femur ....

3   The patella ....

4   The clavicle ....

Inside a flower

Look at this drawing of the parts of a flower. Match the words with the sentences below.

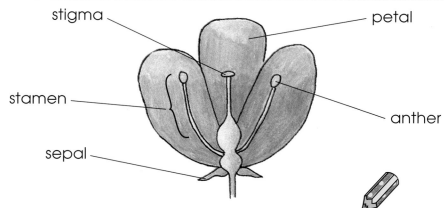

stigma

petal

stamen

anther

sepal

1   The female part of the plant is the ....

2   The male part of the plant is the ....

3   Pollen grains are made in the ....

4   .... attract insects and protect the female and male parts of the plant.

5   .... protect the flower when it is in bud.

Find a flower and look for the different parts. Make a detailed drawing and label it.

You could:

   Count how many petals your flower has.

   Record what colour it is.

   Record where you found it.

   Record if there were any insects nearby and what they were.

Make a table under your drawing like this:

Name	
Colour	
Height	
Number of petals	
Location	
Any insects nearby?	

Variety

Animals and plants of one **species** or type can vary from one to another.

Look at these different dogs. They are all dogs but vary in the way they look. What differences can you see?

  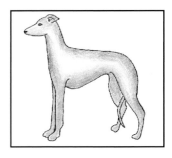 

1 ....

2 ....

3 ....

4 ....

Look at these plants. They are all types of daisy. What are the differences?

1 ....

2 ....

3 ....

4 ....

Collect together some pictures of different types of cats or sheep. What differences can you see in the same species?

Condensation

When you heat water it turns from a **liquid** into a **gas**. This is called steam. Steam is made up of tiny drops of water called water vapour.

If the tiny drops of water touch a cold surface such as a mirror or window they turn back into larger drops of water. This is called **condensation.** You can see this when a plane crosses the sky. The white trail behind the aircraft is made by condensation.

1 Fill a glass with water. Put it into the fridge for two hours. Bring it out and record what happens.

....

....

2 What is happening here?

....

....

....

....

....

....

....

....

....

....

3 Unscramble these words:

DENCONSE .... RAPOUV ....

PLEDTRO .... MEATS ....

Can you find any more examples of condensation taking place?

The water cycle

The air contains a lot of invisible water droplets. Much of this has come from water **evaporating** from the sea. The invisible water droplets rise up into the air. High up they cool and form drops of water as they **condense**. These drops of water form clouds. The clouds are blown by the wind onto the land. When the clouds reach a hill or mountain, the water starts to fall as rain or snow. The rain collects in rivers and flows back to the sea. This is called the **water cycle**.
Look at this picture below. It shows the water cycle.

Write in the boxes what is happening in each part of the picture.

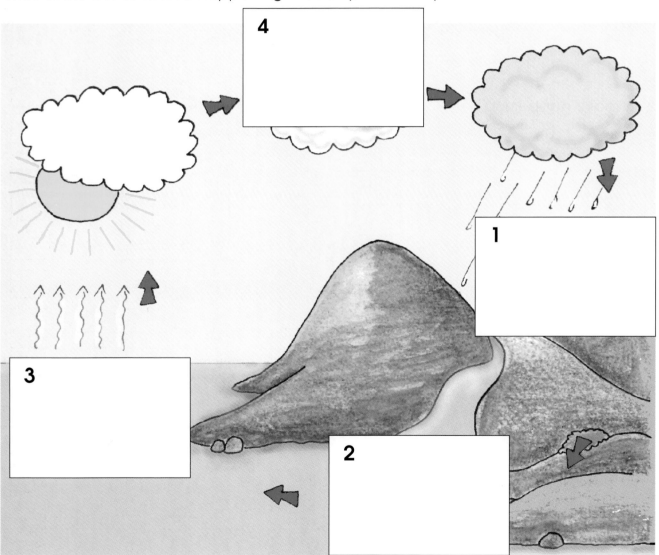

Solids, liquids and gases

If you heat water up to 100°C it boils and turns into a gas. If you cool it below 0°C it freezes and becomes a solid.

Solids have a certain shape and size.

Liquids have a certain size but no certain shape. You can pour a liquid into a glass or other container and it takes on that shape.

Gases do not have a certain size or shape. They will quickly fill any space such as a room.

Look at the list below. Tick if they are solids, liquids or gases.

	liquid	solid	gas
Steam			
Ice			
Water			
Steel			
Oil			
Carbon dioxide			
Wood			
Oxygen			
Copper			
Clay			
Hydrogen			
Tin			
Milk			
Nitrogen			

Microchips

A large number of items in the home use **microchips**. You may have your own computer or radio controlled toy.

Look at the drawing below. Circle the appliances that might use a microchip or computer technology.

Draw a picture of how computers might be used in the home in 100 years' time.

Electrical circuits

Look at the circuits below. Tick the ones that will work.

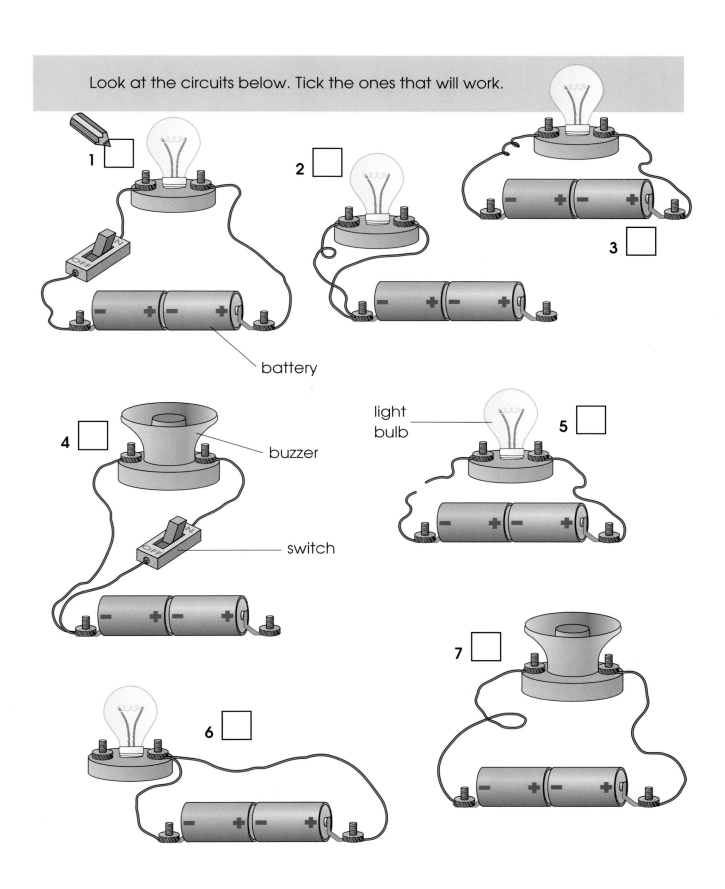

1

2

3

battery

4

buzzer

light
bulb

5

switch

6

7

Sound waves

banjo

When sound travels through the air it causes vibrations.
These are called **sound waves**. If you hit a drum with a stick it will cause the skin of the drum to vibrate. If the string of a violin is plucked this produces vibrations.

Look at these instruments. Which make high and which make low sounds?

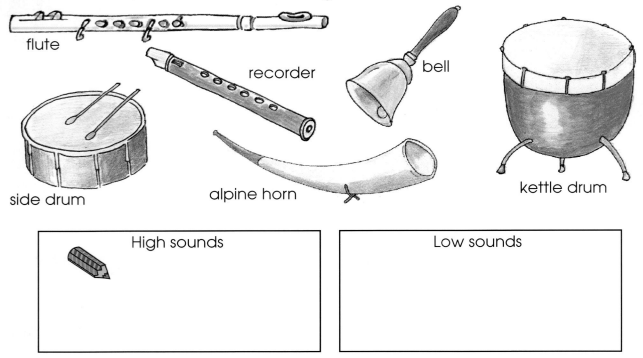

flute

recorder

bell

side drum

alpine horn

kettle drum

High sounds	Low sounds

There are 8 notes in a musical scale. It is called an **octave**. Find out the notes in scale C.

When sound waves hit something they often bounce back towards you. We hear this sound as an **echo**.

Which of these creatures use echoes to find their way:

whale ☐   bat ☐   dolphin ☐

rabbit ☐   worm ☐   dog ☐

Loudness

Noise is measured in decibels.

Put these sounds in order with the faintest first and the loudest last. Fill in the number of decibels each makes. The first three have been done for you.

Decibels: 20   50   70   90   100   200

| 8 | A passing aircraft. | | 150 | decibels |

| 1 | The wind blowing the leaves on a tree. | | 10 | decibels |

| 4 | People shouting. | | 60 | decibels |

| | A road drill. | | | decibels |

| | People talking normally. | | | decibels |

| | A busy city street. | | | decibels |

| | People whispering. | | | decibels |

| | A rocket launching. | | | decibels |

| | A stereo playing. | | | decibels |

Units of measurement

When we measure things we have to decide which kind of **units** we will use. For example you would not measure the distance from London to New York in centimetres or the weight of a blue whale in grammes.

Look at this list of units of measurement:

centimetres, grammes, litres, metres, kilogrammes, Celsius, kilometres, millimetres.

Which unit would you use for each of these tasks:

1   Weighing an elephant.

2   The distance from London to Tokyo by plane.

3   The length of a beetle's leg.

4   The temperature at midday.

5   The weight of a packet of biscuits.

6   The length of your foot.

7   The amount of fuel from a petrol pump.

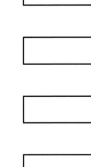

8   Your body's temperature.

9   The length of a garden.

Plotting a graph

Use the information below to finish plotting the straight line graph.

Rainfall recorded in millimetres:

January	43	July	20
February	35	August	23
March	40	September	50
April	43	October	65
May	46	November	69
June	25	December	62

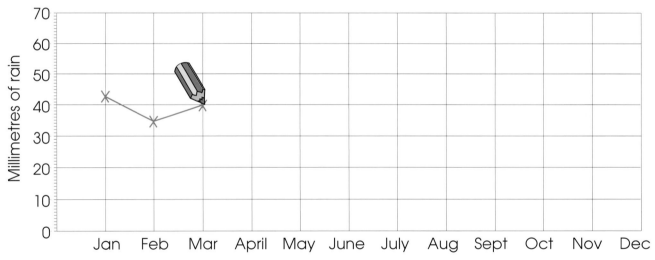

Answer these questions:

1   Which month had the highest rainfall? ....

2   Which month had the lowest rainfall? ....

3   When was the wettest time of the year? ....

4   How many months had under 30 millimetres of rain? ....

5   Was Sepember a wet or dry month? ....

Plot a straight line graph showing how long it takes you to get to school each day over one week.

Blood

Blood may look red, but it is made mainly of **plasma** which is a yellowy colour. Blood also contains **red** and **white blood cells**. The red ones help to carry oxygen around the body. The white ones help to fight off disease.

Blood is taken around the body in three ways:
Arteries carry blood from the heart around the body.
Veins return blood back to the heart.
Capillaries are tiny vessels that carry food and oxygen to the cells of the body and collect waste.

Blood travels quite slowly through your veins. Some of these have special **valves** to stop the blood from falling back towards your feet. Veins are thinner than arteries.

If you cut yourself your blood flows out of the cut and then stops. This is called **clotting**. The blood clot stops any more blood from flowing out. Tiny blood cells called **platelets** help to make your blood clot.

Answer these questions:

1   What is blood made from? ....

2   Name two ways blood is taken around the body. ....

....

3   What pumps blood around your body? ....

4   What colour are the two different types of blood cells? ....

5   What are their jobs? ....

....

6   What happens if you cut yourself? ....

7   Does blood travel fast or slow through the veins? ....

8   Which are thicker, arteries or veins? ....

9   What stops the blood falling back to your feet? ....

10   What are blood clotting cells called? ....

Forces

A **force** is something that pushes or pulls. Forces often produce movement. Things stay still unless a force pushes or pulls them. When a force pushes one way, another force always pulls in the opposite direction.

When this footballer kicks the ball there are two forces that act on the ball. Mark the direction of these two forces beside the football.

Engines are used to produce strong forces. A huge lorry can be moved along by its engine. The hot gas from the back of a rocket engine forces it upwards.

Draw four different types of engines below, showing how the force produced by the engine can make things move. One could be a racing car or a rocket.

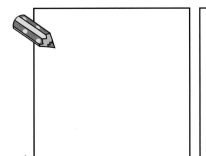

Growth

As living things grow they change. Look at the things below. Draw the way they will change during their lives.

	Stage 1	Stage 2	Stage 3
Frog			
Plant			
Human			
Butterfly			
Bird			
Fish			

How does a caterpillar change into a butterfly?

....

....

Protecting our environment

Match the words with their meanings by filling in the numbers.

A		B		C		D		E		F		G	

A acid rain

B CFCs

C organic farming

D ozone layer

E renewable energy

F recycling

G smog

---

1 Chemicals found in some aerosols, fridges and packing. They can destroy the ozone layer.

2 Energy that is produced from the sun, wind and tides. Sources of energy that will not run out.

3 Using natural things to help plants grow and to control weeds and pests.

4 Rain that contains chemicals which damage trees, plants, animals and buildings. It is caused by pollution.

5 The upper layer of the Earth's atmosphere which contains ozone gas that cuts out harmful rays from the sun.

6 Air pollution from the exhaust fumes of cars and factories.

7 Taking waste and turning it into something that can be used again.

Magnetic forces

There are lines of force around a magnet. To see the pattern of this force place a magnet underneath a piece of paper. Sprinke some iron filings on the paper. Where do most of the filings stick?

Draw in the patterns made by the iron filings.

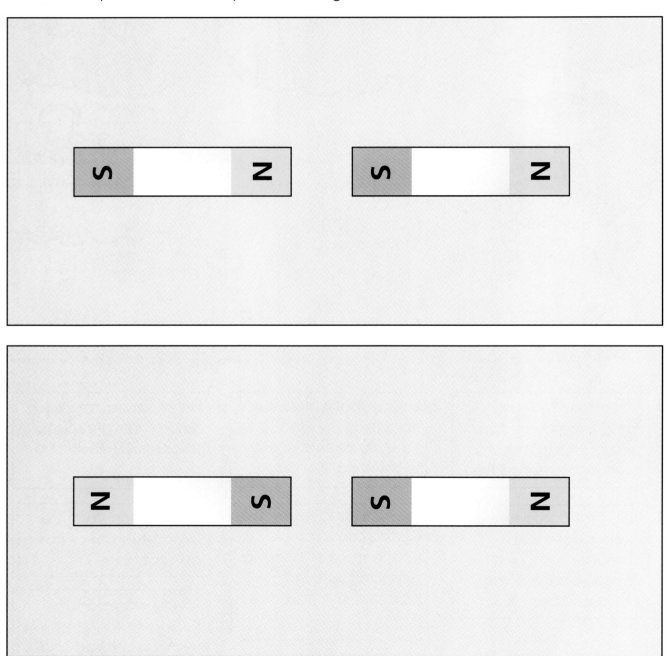

Ecosystems

hawk

Around our homes and schools there are **ecosystems** where creatures and plants work together. These ecosystems each contain many **food webs**. Green plants are the start of a food web. They are called **producers** because they make their own food. Creatures that eat plants are called **primary consumers**. **Secondary consumers** eat primary consumers.

Look at the creatures below and sort them into primary consumers and secondary consumers.

snail

greenfly

cat

thrush

owl

fox

worm

rabbit

dog

ladybird

human

mouse

caterpillar

Primary consumers	Secondary consumers

Reading a table

Sn **Ag** **Pb** **Fe** **Zn** **Al** **Cu** **Au**

Answer the questions about metals below using this table.

Material	Symbol	Properties	Uses
Copper	Cu	Good conductor of electricity; does not rust easily.	Wire; cable; water pipes.
Gold	Au	Found as a pure metal; soft; does not rust; very valuable.	Jewellery; fountain pen nibs; gold teeth.
Aluminium	Al	Good conductor of heat and electricity; can be bent; does not rust.	Saucepans; tinfoil; cans; aircraft; toothpaste tubes.
Iron	Fe	Strong; hard; attracted to a magnet; conducts heat and electricity.	Bridges; knives and forks; pins; screws; ships.
Silver	Ag	Soft; valuable; conducts heat and electricity.	Jewellery; tableware; coins.
Zinc	Zn	Hard; brittle; not affected much by water.	Used in making brass; coating things; paints.
Tin	Sn	Soft; bends easily; can be shaped; doesn't rust easily.	Cans; used to make bronze; many different uses.
Lead	Pb	Very heavy; soft; low melting point.	Batteries; glass; pewter.

1 What is the symbol for silver? _____

2 Is tin a hard metal? _____

3 Does copper conduct electricity? _____

4 What is iron used for? _____

5 Which metal has the symbol Zn? _____

6 Name two conductors of electricity. _____

7 Which metal can be bent and will not rust? _____

8 Which metal is used in batteries? _____

9 Name two metals which are valuable and soft. _____

What happens to a plant if?

Plants will search for light and grow towards it. These experiments show how plants grow to where light is.

1 Place a sprouting potato in a shoe box. Fix some pieces of card in the box. Put the lid on. What happens after a few days? ....

....

2 Why? ....

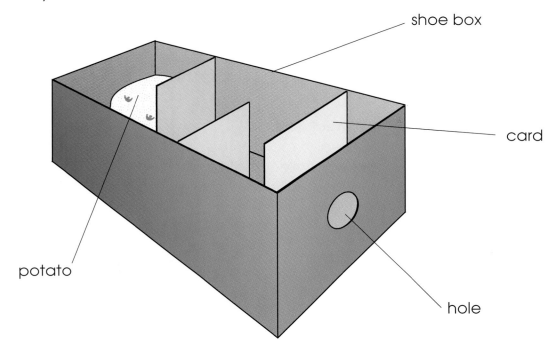

shoe box

card

potato

hole

3 Place a runner bean in a jar. Put in some damp kitchen towel. Put the jar somewhere light and warm. After a week lay the jar on its side. What happens to the roots and shoots?

....

....

4 Why? ....

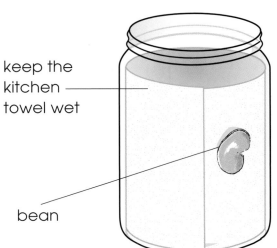

keep the kitchen towel wet

bean

Rocks

Adult supervision needed!

Rocks can be hard or soft. Granite is a very hard rock, but chalk is very soft. Rocks also come in many different colours. Collect together some pebbles or rocks and sort them into different types. Try these two tests.

1 Scratch test

With an adult, try scratching each rock with:
your fingernail
a coin
an old knife
a steel file

Hardness scale	
1 - 2	Scratched with fingernail
3	Scratched with 10p coin
4 - 5	Scratched with knife
6 - 7	Scratched with file
8 - 10	Rock will scratch glass

Using the hardness scale, how hard was your rock?
Write down your results.

2 Streak test

Rub each rock on the back of an old white tile. What colour mark does the rock make? Write down your results.

Name of rock	Scratch test	Streak test

Try the scratch and streak test on other rocks.

Keeping fit

To keep fit we need to take in **vitamins**. These are found in foods. We only need a small amount of them. Here are some important ones.

Vitamin	Used for	Found in
A	Needed for good eyesight to help you see at night.	Carrots.
B	Keeps your blood and nerves healthy.	Meat, bread, eggs and milk.
C	Important for your blood, skin and to help heal your body after an injury.	Oranges and lemons and green vegetables.
D	Important for strong bones.	Eggs and oily fish such as sardines.
E	Keeps your blood and body healthy.	Eggs, nuts, green vegetables, vegetable oil and seeds.

Fill in the vitamins you get from these foods

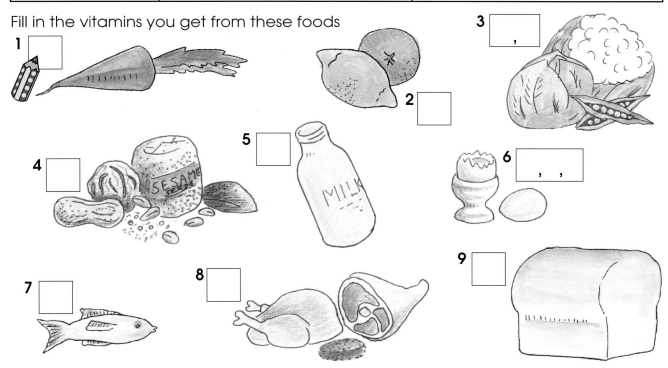

Night and day

The Earth spins round once every 24 hours. For half of this time, one side of the Earth is facing towards the sun and for the other half it is facing away from the sun.

We call the time it is facing towards the sun **day**, and the time it is facing away **night.**

Draw two diagrams below to show how this happens.

Day

Night

Muscles

Whenever you move you use your muscles. There are over 650 muscles in the body. You use them to wave, blink, run, talk or smile.

Muscles can pull, but not push. Many work in pairs. If you exercise your muscles you can make them stronger. Athletes and football players need to exercise their muscles to give them strength.

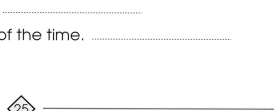

Mark on the figure where you would find these muscles:

biceps

calf muscles

thigh muscles

neck muscles

Some muscles work all the time, others have to be told when to work.

Name a muscle that works all the time.

....

Are these sentences right or wrong?

1   Muscles can push and pull. ....

2   There are more than 650 muscles in our bodies. ....

3   The biceps are found in our arms. ....

4   Many muscles work in threes. ....

5   Sportsmen and women do not need to exercise their muscles. ....

6   The heart works all of the time. ....

7   You do not use muscles when you blink. ....

8   You will make your muscles stronger by exercise. ....

9   There are no muscles in your neck. ....

10   You have no muscles that work all of the time. ....

Reflected light

When a ray of light hits something it will bounce off it. Look in a mirror and you will see your **reflection**. Mirrors are made from materials that reflect light easily. Try this experiment to show that light reflects off a mirror at the same angle as it strikes it. It should be done in a dark room.

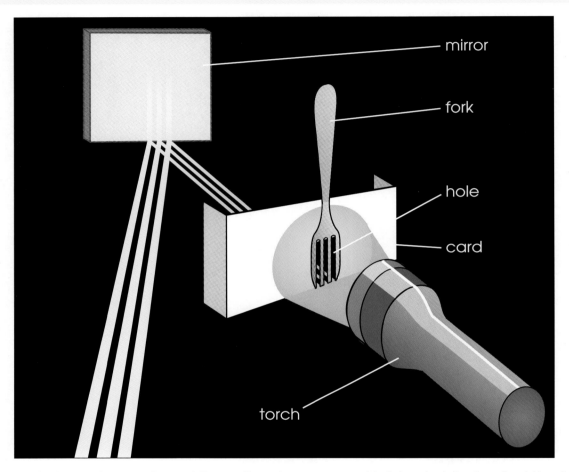

Make a hole in a piece of card 5 centimetres across. Hold a fork in front of the hole. Get a friend to shine a torch from behind the card so that the beam goes through the fork and is reflected in the mirror. See if you can change the angle of the beam of light by moving the mirror.

Materials with a shiny surface are good at reflecting light. Tick the materials below that would make good reflectors.

silver ✓   aluminium ☐   newspaper ☐

black paper ☐   bronze ☐

What does this show?

Write down what has changed in the second picture and why this might have happened.

1 ....
....
....
....
....

2 ....
....
....
....
....

3 ....
....
....
....
....

4 ....
....
....
....

5 ....
....
....
....

6 ....
....
....
....

Looking after your teeth

It is important that we look after our teeth and keep them clean. This will stop them being attacked by bacteria.

How do these things help keep your teeth healthy or harm them?

1 ....

2 ....

3 ....

4 ....

5 ....

6 ....

7 ....

8 ....

9 ....

Elastic band boat

Elastic bands can be used to store **energy**.

The paddle on this boat is made from an elastic band. When twisted it stores up energy. When it is released the energy is used to move the boat across the water.

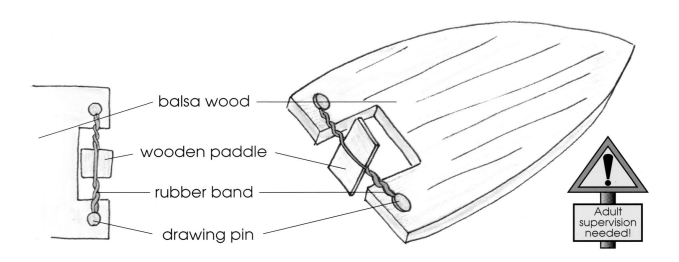

balsa wood

wooden paddle

rubber band

drawing pin

Adult
supervision
needed!

With an adult, cut out the shape of a boat from a piece of balsa wood. Cut out a piece at the back of the boat as shown. Fix on two drawing pins. Fix an elastic band between them. Slide in a small piece of balsa wood to act as a paddle. Twist the paddle round and round until the rubber band is really tight. Put your boat in some water and let the paddle go. Watch what happens. Record your results below.

....

....

....

....

What other forms of energy could you use to power your boat?

....

Friction

Friction stops things from sliding around. The smoother the surface of an object, the lower the friction.

Make a slope using a piece of wood and two bricks.

Put a small wooden block at the top. Let it go. What happens?

....

Wet the slope. Try again. What happens?

....

Rub soap on the slope. Try again. What happens?

....

What other ways can you think of reducing friction?

....

Fill in this table. Put the object at the top of your slope. Let it go. Was it a very good, good or bad mover down the slope?

Object	Dry slope	Wet slope	Soaped slope
Ball			
Rubber			
Paper cup			
Ruler			
Toy with wheels			
Pencil			

Questionnaire

Answer these questions. All of the answers can be found in this book.

1   Is oxygen a solid, liquid or gas? ....

2   A ball falls to the ground because of ....

3   What are animals that eat plants called? ....

4   The symbol for tin is ....

5   Vitamin C is found in ....

6   The Earth spins once every ....

7   When a baby is born its bones are very ....

8   Muscles pull, they cannot ....

9   Noise is measured in ....

10 Solids have a certain size and ....

11 We have .... and .... blood cells in our bodies.

12 Acid rain can damage trees and ....

13 Copper is used to make pipes and ....

14 Water boils at ....°C.

15 What is another name for the femur? ....

16 The water cycle explains why .... and .... fall.

17 If sound bounces back what do we call it? ....

18 Are veins thinner than arteries? ....

19 Is granite a hard or soft rock? ....

20 What are platelets? ....

21 Where would you find the ozone layer? ....

22 Which vitamins are found in eggs? ....

23 Where is the patella? ....

24 Which is louder, a road drill or a passing aircraft? ....

25 Why does tinfoil make a good reflector? ....

Answers

Page 2

1 skull;   **2** scapula;   **3** rib;
4 radius and ulna; **5** femur; **6** clavicle;
7 spine;   **8** humerus;   **9** pelvis;
10 patella; **11** tibia and fibula.
1 shoulder blade; **2** thigh bone;
3 kneecap;   **4** collar bone.

Page 3

1 stigma;   **2** stamen;   **3** anther;
4 Petals;   **5** Sepals.

Page 4

Differences for dogs could include: length of hair, colour, size, length of legs, size and type of ears etc.
Differences for daisies could include: colour of flowers, prickles, shape of flowers, number of petals, shape of leaves etc.

Page 5

1 Water droplets form on the outside of the glass. This happens because the cold water in the glass cools the air around it and some of the water vapour in the air is turned to drops of water on the glass.
2 When the steam from the hot bath touches the cold surface of the window, the steam is turned into drops of water.
3 CONDENSE   VAPOUR
    DROPLET   STEAM

Page 6

1 Rain or snow falls from clouds on mountains and high ground.
2 The rain runs into streams and rivers which flow down to the sea.
3 The water evaporates from the surface of the sea. It rises as water vapour.
4 The water vapour forms clouds as it condenses. The clouds are blown by the wind back towards the land.

Page 7

steam/gas;   ice/solid;   water/liquids;
steel/solid;   oil/liquid;
carbon dioxide/gas;   wood/solid;
oxygen/gas;   copper/solid;
clay/solid;   hydrogen/gas;
tin/solid;   milk/liquid;   nitrogen/gas.

Page 8

Television, clock, radio alarm clock, stereo, video, remote control, computer, portable phone, calculator, central heating thermostat, microwave oven, coffee percolator, dishwasher, electric oven, digital watch, toy car, washing machine, fan, vacuum cleaner, clock.

Page 9

1 yes;   **2** no;   **3** yes;   **4** no;
5 no;   **6** no;   **7** yes.

Page 10

High sounds: recorder, banjo, flute, bell, side drum.
Low sounds: Alpine horn, kettle drum.
Scale C: C D E F G A B C
whale, bat, dolphin.

Page 11

2 People whispering 20 decibels
3 People talking normally 50 decibels
5 A stereo playing 70 decibels
6 A busy city street 90 decibels
7 A road drill 100 decibels
9 A rocket launching 200 decibels.

Page 12

1 kilogrammes;   **2** kilometres;
3 millimetres;   **4** Celsius;
5 grammes;   **6** centimetres;
7 litres;   **8** Celsius;   **9** metres.

Page 13

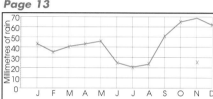

1 November;   **2** July;   **3** October to December;   **4** 3 months;   **5** wet.

Page 14

1 mainly of plasma *or* plasma, red and white blood cells and platelets.
2 Two from: arteries, veins and capillaries
3 The heart.   **4** Red and white.
5 Red blood cells carry oxygen and white blood cells fight off disease.
6 The blood clots.   **7** Slow.   **8** Arteries.
9 Special valves in your veins. **10** Platelets.

Page 15

Page 16

Frog

Plant

Human

Butterfly

Bird

Fish

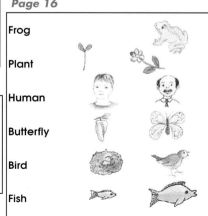

The caterpillar becomes a chrysalis. Inside the chrysalis it changes and emerges as a butterfly.

Page 17

A 4;   B 1;   C 3;   D 5;   E 2;
F 7;   G 6.

Page 18

Page 19

Primary consumers: worm, snail, greenfly, caterpillar, rabbit, mouse.
Secondary consumers: fox, thrush, hawk, ladybird, cat, dog, owl, human.

Page 20

1 Ag;   **2** no;   **3** yes;
4 Making bridges, knives and forks, pins, screws and ships;   **5** zinc;
6 Two from: iron, copper, aluminium and silver;   **7** aluminium or tin;
8 lead;   **9** gold and silver.

Page 21

1 As the shoots of the potato start to grow they will find their way around the maze. (If you are successful the shoots should come out of the hole at the end of the box.)
2 The shoots are searching for the light.
3 The roots should grow downwards and the shoots should grow upwards.
4 The shoots are drawn towards the light and the roots are pulled downwards by gravity.

Page 23

1 A;   **2** C;   **3** C, E;
4 E;   **5** B;   **6** B, D, E;
7 D;   **8** B;   **9** B.

Page 24

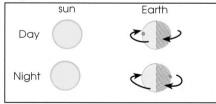

Page 25

neck muscles   the heart
    1 wrong;
biceps   **2** right;
    3 right;
    4 wrong;
thigh muscles   **5** wrong;
    6 right;
    7 wrong;
calf muscles   **8** right;
    9 wrong;
    10 wrong.

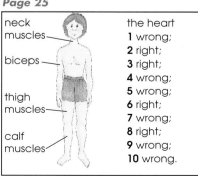